# Ozzy the Fox

**Michael Farrell**
**Laura Renfrew**

The not so cunning Ozzy the Fox lives under a tree, in the forest, not far from Goldilocks.

He was always so hungry and getting up to no good, but for all his mad ideas, Ozzy the Fox could never catch any food.

He spent days at the river trying
to catch Freddie the Fish.

Well Freddie was so slippery and to catch
him he could only dream, he could only wish.

He waited till dark, to creep up on Axle
the Owl perched high in his tree.

Didn't he know that's when
an Owl can best see?

Next in the forest he came across
Jimi the Raccoon, with an empty
belly he better eat soon.

He wore a burglar jumper and mask
trying to disguise but that raccoon
also bites, so that wasn't wise.

To get close to Kurt the Frog he painted
himself green. He thought he could sit
on a lily pad... he was far too keen.

Then he covered himself in feathers to get close
to the farmer's chickens, dug under their house
where he though it would be easy pickings.

But that house belonged to a dog and that's where the plot thickens.

He tried to climb a great tree to sneak up on Alice and Dave the Squirrels. They couldn't contain their laughter as they watched him take a twirl.

Ozzy flattened his tail to look like
Rodger the beaver, but silly Ozzy
the Fox was just too eager.

He strapped springs to his feet to keep up
with Mick the Rabbit, others in the forest
thought he might have just grabbed it.

But hungry Ozzy only got a hold of his jacket.

Now he was getting desperate and slithered and hissed and went after Iggy the Snake.

Everyone in the forest knew that was a big mistake.

Ozzy the Fox should have looked closer to home, around his tree is where he should have roamed. As around that tree was apples that dropped, he didn't have to cover himself in feathers or hiss or hop.

He picked an apple up took a bite and to his
surprise, felt his taste buds go into overdrive.
As he started to take a look around, he
noticed other gems growing in the ground.

There were carrots, potatoes, turnips - the lot!
Broccoli, mushrooms, tomatoes and shallots.

Now around that tree a garden he has grew and all the animals in the forest queue, for a bowl of Ozzy's now famous vegetable stew.

# The End

# Colouring Pages

Printed in Great Britain
by Amazon

47884099R10015